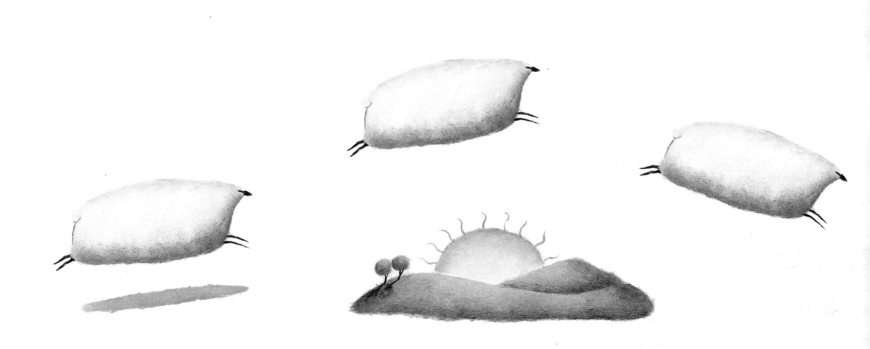

William
and the
NIGHT - TRAIN

Written by   Illustrated by

Mij Kelly   Alison Jay

*Hodder
Children's
Books*

A division of Hodder Headline Limited

To Ma and Pa
M.K.

To James William
A.J.

British Library Cataloguing in Publication Data
A catalogue record of this book is available from the British Library

ISBN 0 340 73308 X (HB)
ISBN 0 340 73250 4 (PB)

First UK edition published in 2000
by Hodder Children's Books
a division of Hodder Headline Limited
338 Euston Road London NW1 3BH

10 9 8 7 6 5 4 3 2 1

Printed in Hong Kong

'All aboard!'
shouts the guard.
'All aboard
the night-train.
All aboard
the train that
goes to Tomorrow.'

teachers and jugglers, zoo keepers, shopkeepers,

Mothers and fathers, sisters and brothers,

They're all sleepy-heads, all ready for bed,

writers and fighters, with babies in bundles and piglets in baskets — they all climb aboard.

all on their way to Tomorrow . . .

. . . with wide-awake
William, who wants
to get there most
of all.

The goods van is stacked with boxes and sacks,

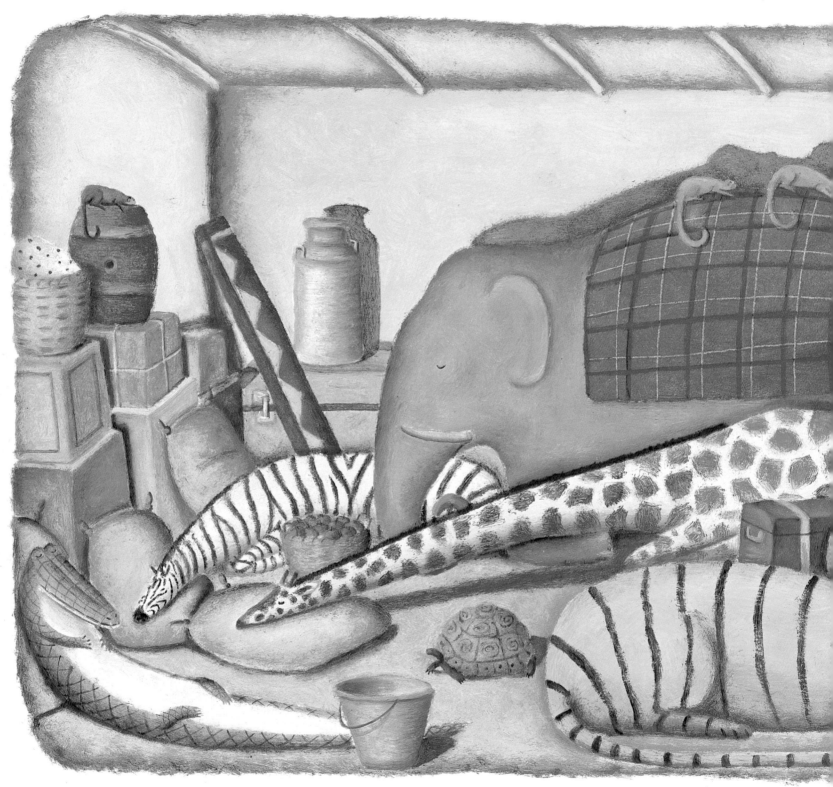

five sleepy monkeys and a huge slumbering cat.

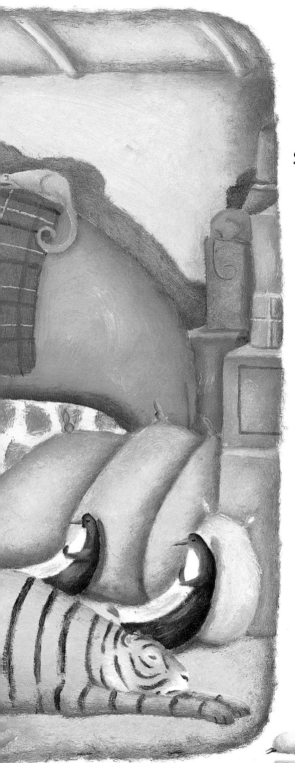

'Everyone
sleeps on the
night-train,'
says William's
mother.
But William
squirms like
a worm.
He wriggles.
He kicks.
He wants to
get to
Tomorrow.
He wants
to get there
quick.

The guard's van is crammed
like a box of delights with balloons and kites,

and bright
secret packages
bundled up tight.

'Everyone sleeps on the
night-train,' yawns the guard.

But William's in such a giddy rush he doesn't want
to have to hush. He doesn't care if he makes
a row. He's wide awake.
He wants to get to Tomorrow NOW.

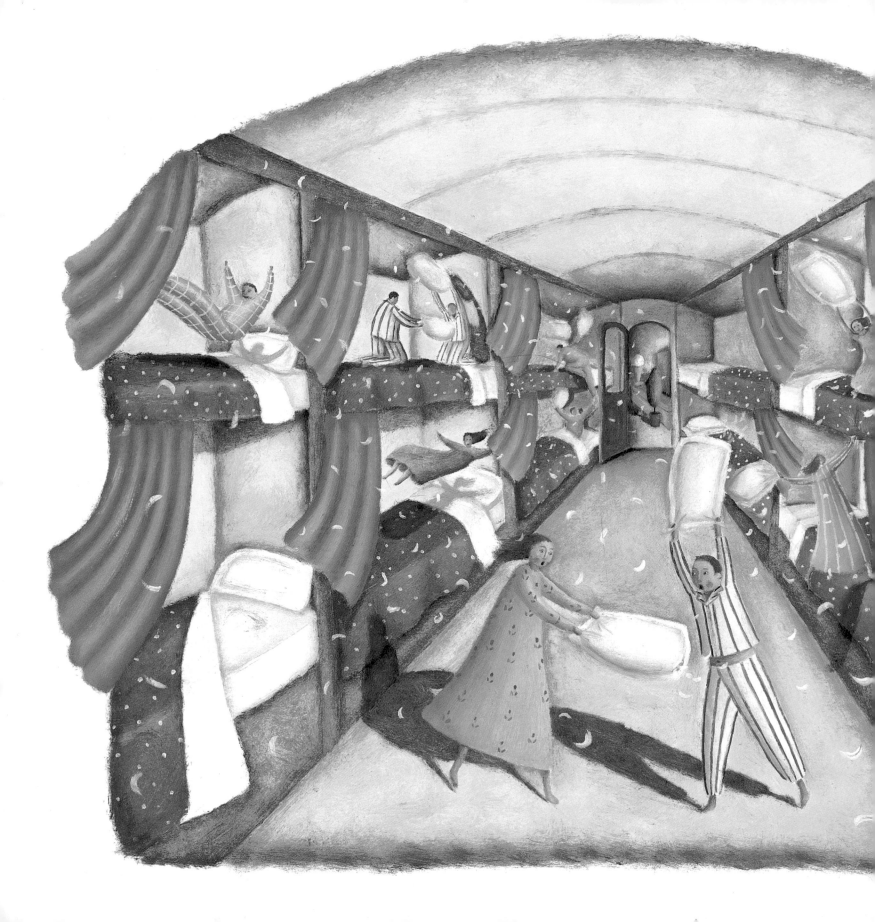

In the sleeping compartments, children bounce on their beds and hurl feather pillows at each other's heads.

'Everyone sleeps on the night-train,' sighs the teacher.

But William just laughs and charges on past. He whirls through the feathers; he's switched on like a light. He wants to get to Tomorrow in the middle of the night.

In the carriages people sit nodding in rows. They slumber and doze. They're not wearing pyjamas; they're still in their clothes!

'Everyone sleeps on the night-train,' explains the writer.

But William's too busy squishing his nose. He's too busy standing on tippity toes. He's too wide awake. All he knows is that he can't wait for the train to go.

'When will we get to Tomorrow?'

Then his mother tells him about a trick that will make the night-train go lickety-split, helter-skelter, quick as a streak.

'Shut those wide-awake eyes,' she whispers.
'And shh, don't speak.'

When she cuddles him close he can hear her heart and

a soft, sudden whoosh as the night-train starts.

It pulls out of the station and into the dark,
filling the world with billows of steam,
soft see-through clouds that turn into dreams.

baskets and babies in bundles, brothers and mothers and all

Teachers and jugglers, sacks, cats and packages, piglets in

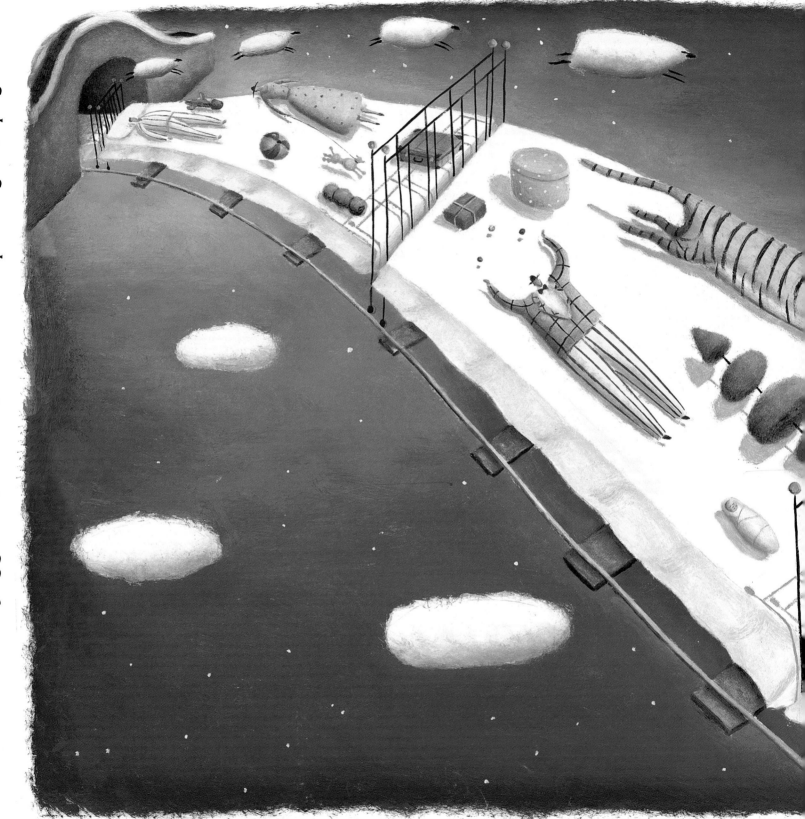

of the others speed out of today in the blink of an eye. Everyone sleeps on the night-train on the way to Tomorrow . . .

. . . even
sleepy-head
William,
who wants to
get there
most of all.

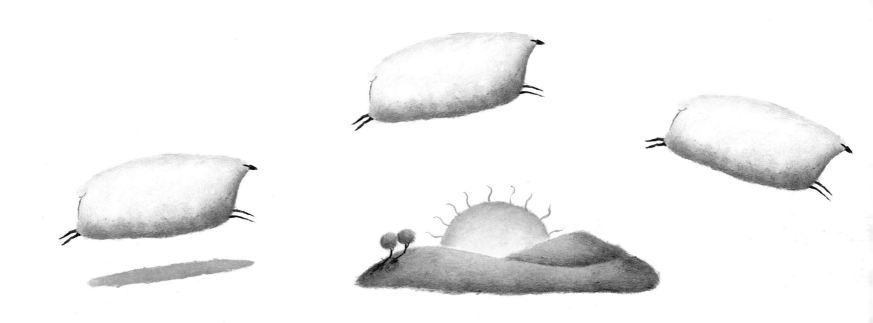